SUDOKU PUZZLES

Volume 8

		6		3				
4		7	1				2	6
	8		2	5		7	4	1
2	6	3	7		8	5		4
	4						9	
5		1	6		3	2	7	8
9	7	4		6	5		3	
8	3				1	4		7
				7		9		

KAPPA Books
A Division of KAPPA Graphics, LP

For more puzzle fun go to www.kappapuzzles.com

INTRODUCTION

Sudoku is the biggest puzzle craze in years. The puzzles themselves have been around for many years in the U.S. and elsewhere under many different names, but they really caught fire in Japan during the 1990s. They were dubbed “su doku,” which is an abbreviated form of a Japanese expression meaning “single number.” Now, people all over the world are discovering how enjoyable and addictive solving sudoku puzzles can be.

The rules are simple. A quick look at this book reveals that each puzzle is a 9-by-9 grid of squares divided into nine 3-by-3 square blocks, with some of the squares filled in for you. The object is to fill in the blank squares in such a way that each of the numbers 1 to 9 appears exactly once in each row, column, and block. If the puzzle has been constructed properly, there should be only one way to complete the diagram within the rules of the game. Despite this apparent simplicity, solving some sudoku puzzles can be complicated indeed.

The rest of this introduction is dedicated to explaining the three most basic strategies the solver can employ. All but the simplest puzzles will require the use of each of these techniques, although you may not even be aware that you’re using them. Other, more complicated methods are really just elaborations on these three.

1. ELIMINATION ON SQUARES

The most obvious method involves finding a blank for which only one possible digit remains. For example, the highlighted square in grid A can’t hold a 6, 1, or 3, since those digits are already in its row. Nor can it hold the 4 or 7, since they are already represented in the highlighted square’s column. Likewise, the square can’t hold a 9, 5, or 2, because those numbers are already in its block. The only number from 1 to 9 that isn’t eliminated is 8, so the highlighted square must hold an 8.

							9	5
6	1			3				
								2
						4		
						7		

Grid A

More often than not, when you attempt this elimination method, you will be left with more than one possibility. If no more than three or four such possibilities exist, it can be very useful to lightly pencil in those possibilities in the blank.

2. SOLVING ON POSSIBILITIES IN COMMON

Suppose you have used the “elimination on squares” method and have penciled in partial solutions for three of the blanks in a 3-by-3 block.

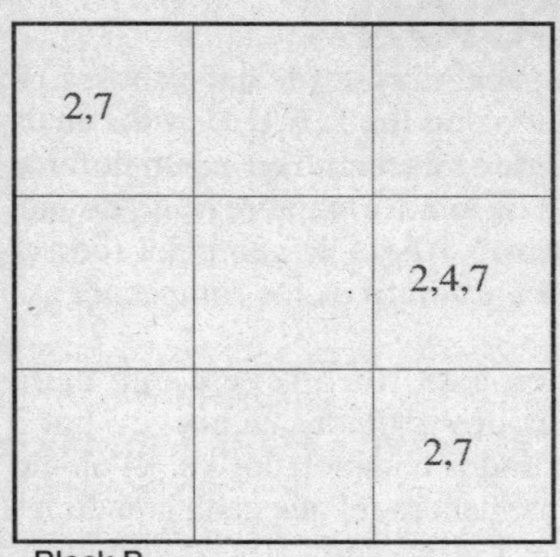

Block B

Suppose further that the possibilities are: 2 and 7 for the first blank; 2, 4, and 7 for the second; and 2 and 7 for the third (see block B). Since the first and third each hold only either 2 or 7, they must hold 2 and 7, in some order. Thus, the second blank can't hold either of those numbers — it would have to hold a 4. Furthermore, none of the other six squares in the block can contain a 2, 4, or 7, so those numbers can be eliminated from their possibility lists. In general, if the combined possibility lists for three blanks in a row, column, or block include no more than three of the numbers from 1 to 9, then no other blanks in the row, column, or block can be any of those three numbers. Likewise for four lists with only four numbers, and so on.

3. ELIMINATION ON NUMBERS

So far, our strategy has been to look for the only number that can be placed in a particular blank. Now we'll use the complementary attack — look for the only blank that can hold a given number. An illustration will help express this idea. We know there must be a 5 in the third horizontal row of grid C. It won't be in any of the three on the left, since a 5 already resides in the top-left block. Likewise, there can't be a 5 in the middle three spaces of the third row. Finally, there can't be a 5 in the seventh spot of the third row, since we already have a 5 in the seventh column. By elimination, the 5 in the third row is in the eighth spot (just to the left of the 4).

		5						
			5					
								4
						5		

Grid C

Another way of doing elimination on numbers happens after you have used the "elimination on squares" method and created lists of possibilities for all of the blanks in an entire row, column, or block. In this case, you may notice that only one of the lists includes the number 6. Thus, a 6 would have to go in that blank.

Armed with these methods and others that you will undoubtedly come up with yourself, you will be solving sudoku puzzles like a pro in no time.

INTRODUCCIÓN

Sudoku es la manía más grande del rompecabezas desde hace años. Los rompecabezas han existido por muchos años en los E.E.U.U. y en otros lugares con nombres distintos, pero realmente se encendió en Japón durante los años 90. Eran llamado ' su doku', que es una forma abreviada de una expresión japonés que significa "solo número". Ahora, la gente por todo el mundo est´n descubriendo cómo agradables y adictivos los rompecabezas del sudoku pueden ser.

Las reglas son simples. Un vistazo en este libro revela que cada rompecabezas es una rejilla de 9 por 9 cuadrados divididos en nueve 3 por 3 bloques cuadrados, con algunos de los cuadrados completados ya. El objeto es completar los cuadrados en blanco de una manera tal que cada uno de los números 1 a 9 aparezca exactamente una vez en cada fila, columna, y bloque. Si el rompecabezas se ha construido correctamente, debe haber solamente una manera de completar el diagrama usando las reglas del juego. A pesar de esta simplicidad evidente, solucionar algunos rompecabezas del sudoku puede ser muy complicado.

El resto de esta introducción se dedica a explicar las tres estrategias más básicas que los jugadores pueden emplear. Todos sino los rompecabezas más simples requerirán el uso de cada uno de estas técnicas, aunque puede ser que no diérese cuenta de que las está utilizando. Otros métodos más complicados son nada mas que elaboraciones por estos tres.

1. ELIMINACIÓN EN CUADRADOS

El método más obvio implica el encontrar de un espacio blanco para el cual solamente hay un dígito posible. Por ejemplo, el cuadrado destacado en la rejilla A no puede tener 6, 1, o 3, puesto que esos dígitos están ya en su fila. Ni puede tener 4 o 7, puesto que se están representados ya en la columna cuadrada destacada. Asimismo, el cuadrado no puede tener 9, 5, o 2, porque esos números están ya en su bloque. El único número a partir de la 1 a 9 que no se elimina es 8, así que el cuadrado destacado debe tener 8.

							9	5
6	1			3		■		
								2
						4		
						7		

Rejilla A

A menudo, cuando se intenta este método de la eliminación, le dejarán con más de una posibilidad. Si existen no más de tres o cuatro tales posibilidades, puede ser muy útil usar lápiz ligeramente en esas posibilidades en el espacio blanco.

2. SOLUCIONAR POSIBILIDADES EN CAMPO COMÚN

Suponga que usted ha utilizado el método "eliminación en cuadrados" y que lo tiene en lápiz las soluciones parciales para tres de los espacios en

2,7		
		2,4,7
		2,7

Bloque B

blanco en un bloque de 3 por 3. Suponga más que las posibilidades son: 2 y 7 para el primer espacio blanco; 2, 4, y 7 para el segundo; y 2 y 7 para el tercero (véase el bloque B). Puesto que el primer y el tercer solamente tiene o 2 o 7, ellos deben tener 2 y 7, en una cierta orden. Así, el segundo espacio en blanco no puede tener ninguno de esos números — tendría que tener 4. Además, ninguno de los otros seis cuadrados en el bloque pueden contener 2, 4, o 7, así que esos números se pueden eliminar de sus lista de posibilidades. Generalmente, si las listas de los posibilidades combinadas para tres blancos en una fila, una columna, o un bloque incluya no más que tres de los números a partir de la 1 a 9, entonces ninguno otro espacio blanco en la fila, la columna, o el bloque puede ser cualesquiera de esos tres números. Asimismo para cuatro listas con solamente cuatro números, y así sucesivamente.

3. ELIMINACIÓN EN NÚMEROS

Hasta ahora, nuestra estrategia ha sido buscar el œnico nœmero que se puede poner en un espacio blanco en particular. Ahora utilizaremos el ataque complementario: buscamos el œnico espacio en blanco que puede tener un número dado. Una ilustración ayudará expresar a esta idea. Sabemos que debe haber 5 en la tercera fila horizontal de la rejilla C. No estará en ninguno de los tres a la izquierda, puesto que 5 reside ya en el bloque tapa-izquierdo. Asimismo, no puede haber 5 en los tres espacios medios de la tercera fila. Finalmente, no puede haber 5 en el séptimo lugar de la tercera fila, puesto que tenemos ya 5 en la séptima columna. Por la eliminación, el 5 en la tercera fila está en el octavo punto (justo a la izquierda del 4).

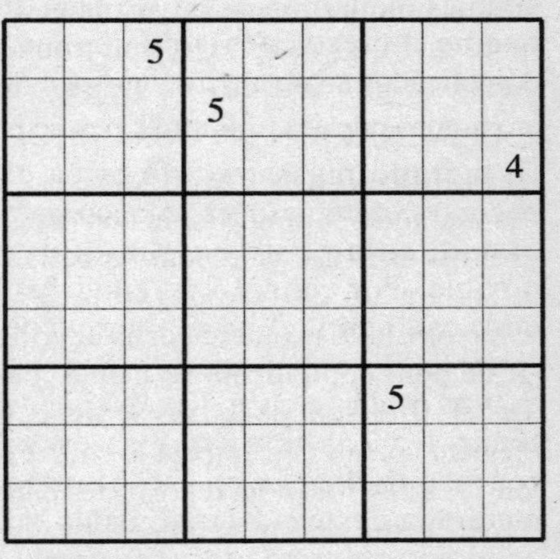

Rejilla C

Otra manera de hacer la eliminación en números sucede después de que usted haya utilizado el método de 'eliminación en cuadrados' y creado listas de las posibilidades de todos los espacios en blanco en una fila, una columna, o un bloque entera. En este caso, usted puede notar que solamente uno de las listas incluye el número 6. Así, 6 tendrían que estar en eso espacio blanco.

Armado con estos métodos y otros que seguramente ocurra a se, usted solucionará rompecabezas del sudoku como un profesional en menos que canta un gallo.

INTRODUCTION

Le Sudoku est un jeu qui existait depuis plus de 20 ans aux États-Unis et ailleurs sous noms différents avant de devenir la fureur qu'il soit aujourd'hui. C'est au Japon que le phénomè a pris naissance dans les années 90. Là-bas on appelle ce jeu «Sudoku»—une expression qui signifie «chiffre unique». Maintenant, les gens à travers tout le monde découvrent comment il est agréable et enivrant de résoudre une grille du jeu de Sudoku.

Les règles sont simples. Un coup d'œil rapide dans ce livret révèlera que la grille de jeu est un carré de neuf cases de côté, subdivisé en neuf carrés identiques (3x3), appelés régions ou blocs. La grille de jeu contient des chiffres de 1 à 9 (les dévoilés) et des cases vides. Le but est de remplir les cases vides avec des chiffres de 1 à 9 en respectant cette règle: chaque ligne, chaque colonne, et chacque région ne doit contenir qu'une seule fois tous les chiffres de 1 à 9. Si une grille a été construite correctement, il y aura seulement une façon de compléter le diagramme. Malgré la simplicité apparente du jeu, il y a des grilles de Sudoku qui sont très difficiles à résoudre.

Le reste de cette introduction est consacré a l'explication des trois stratégies les plus simples qu'un joueur peut utiliser pour résoudre une grille de Sudoku. La résolution des grilles, a l'exception des plus simples, nécessitera l'usage de ces techniques même si parfois vous ne vous rendrez même pas compte que vous en faites usage. On peut trouver des méthodes encore plus complexes, mais en général ces stratégies ne seront plus que des variations et combinaisons des trois stratégies de bases suivantes que nous allons expliquer.

1. ELIMINATION PAR CASES

La méthode la plus simple consiste à trouver une case vide pour laquelle il n'y a qu'un chiffre possible. Par exemple, la case ombrée dans la grille A ne peut contenir un 6, 1 ou 3, car ces chiffres sont déjà dans sa ligne. Il ne peut contenir également le chiffre 4 ou 7, car ils sont déjà représentés dans la colonne où se trouve la case ombrée. De même, le carré ne peut contenir un 9, 5 ou 2, car ces chiffres sont déjà dans cette région. Le seul chiffre de 1 à 9 qui ne soit pas encore éliminé est 8, donc le chiffre manquant dans la case ombrée est obligatoirement un 8.

							9	5
6	1			3				
								2
						4		
						7		

Grille A

Bien souvent, en utilisant cette méthode par élimination, vous vous retrouverez avec plus d'une possibilité. Si pas plus de 3 ou 4 chiffres possibles existent, il peut être très utile à essayer les possibilités différentes avec un crayon à papier.

2. RÉSOUDRE PAR LES POSSIBILTÉS EN COMMUN

Supposons que vous avez utilisé la méthode de «l'élimination en cases»

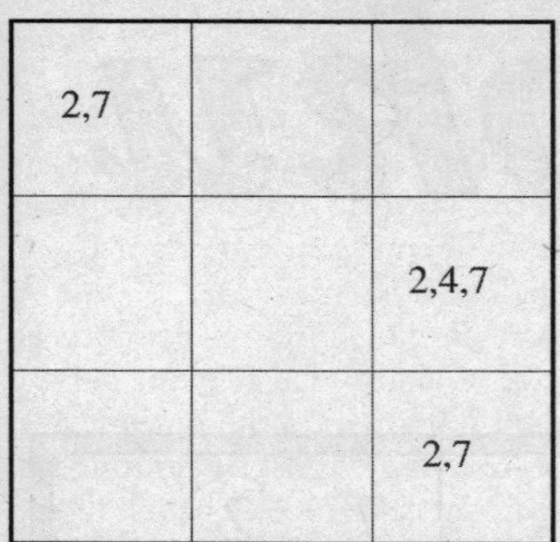

Région B

et que vous avez essayé au crayon des solutions partielles pour trois cases vides dans une région 3x3. Supposons plus loin que les possibilités sont 2 et 7 dans la première case vide; 2, 4 et 7 pour la deuxième; et 2 et 7 pour la troisième (voir la région B). Puisque la première et la troisième contiennent seulement 2 ou 7, ils doivent donc contenir 2 et 7, en quelque ordre. Par conséquent, la deuxième case vide ne peut contenir aucun de ces chiffres. Il devra donc nécessairement contenir le chiffre 4. De plus, aucun des 6 autres cases vides dans la région ne contient un 2, 4 ou 7, donc ces chiffres doivent être éliminés de la liste des possibilités. En général, si la liste des possibilités combinées de trois cases vides dans une ligne, une colonne, ou une région ne contiennent plus que trois chiffres différents, alors aucunes autres cases vides dans la ligne, la colonne, ou la région peut contenir l'un de ces trois chiffres. Il en va ainsi pour quatre listes avec seulement quatre chiffres, etc.

3. ELIMINATION PAR CHIFFRES

		5						
			5					
								4
						5		

Grille C

Jusqu'à présent, notre stratégie a été de rechercher seulement le chiffre unique qui pouvait être placé dans une case vide. Maintenant nous allons utiliser une technique complémentaire: rechercher la case vide qui puisse contenir un chiffre donné. Un exemple nous aidera à mieux comprendre cette idée. Nous savons qu'il doit avoir un 5 dans la troisième ligne de la grille C. Le 5 n'ira dans aucune des trois lignes sur la gauche, car le chiffre 5 se trouve dans cette région déjà. De même, il ne peut pas y avoir de 5 des trois cases au milieu de la troisième ligne, car il y a déjà un 5 dans la septième colonne. Par élimination, le 5 dans la troisième ligne est dans le huitième case (juste à gauche du 4).

Une autre façon d'appliquer «l'élimination par chiffre» arrive après que vous avez utilisé la méthode de «l'élimination par cases» et que vous avez créé une liste de possibilités pour toutes les cases vides dans une ligne, une colonne, ou une région. En ce cas, si vous remarquez qu'il n'y a qu'une liste avec le chiffre 6, vous saurez mettre le chiffre 6 à cette case.

Armés de ces méthodes et d'autres que vous allez découvrir vous-même, vous resolverez des grilles de Sudoku comme pro bientôt.

sudoku

★

	4		1			7	2	
1	2	6				5	4	8
7	9			4	2	3		
	5			7	4		3	2
3			2		8			5
4	6		3	1			8	
		7	5	8			9	4
5	8	9				6	7	3
	3	4			9		5	

Puzzle 1

Solution on 127

sudoku

★

	9		3			5		
6		8						4
3		4	7	1	8			6
	3	7	9	6		8	1	2
		2	8		4	9		
5	8	9		3	2	4	6	
7			2	9	1	6		5
8						7		9
		5			7		4	

Puzzle 2

Solution on 127

sudoku

★

9	6	7			2			
	3		6	9	4	2	5	7
4	2		7					
		9	1	5				3
	8	6	9		7	4	1	
1				3	8	9		
					1		4	2
2	7	8	3	4	5		6	
			2			7	3	8

Puzzle 3

Solution on 127

sudoku

★

2		3		6		4		
6		4	9		1		8	3
			2		3	6		5
7	2		3		4			6
1			5		2			4
3			1		6		2	9
8		2	4		5			
5	9		6		7	3		8
		7		3		1		2

Puzzle 4

Solution on 127

sudoku

★

			6	7	5			3
	5		9		3			
6		9		8	4			7
9		4	7		1	2	8	
2		1				3		9
	8	5	4		2	7		1
4			3	2		1		8
			1		8		3	
8			5	6	9			

Puzzle 5

Solution on 127

sudoku

★

	6		5	7	2	1		3
5					3		2	9
		2		9		7	6	5
4	8				7	6	1	
				3				
	2	6	1				5	7
3	1	5		8		2		
2	4		7					1
6		7	3	2	1		8	

Puzzle 6

Solution on 128

sudoku

☆

		6				5		
		3	2	1	5	6		4
	1	5	6		9		2	7
	8	9	3	5		7	6	
	3		9		2		4	
	4	7		6	1	9	3	
1	6		7		8	2	5	
3		8	1	2	6	4		
		2				1		

Puzzle 7

Solution on 128

sudoku

★

		4	2	6			7	
	5				1			4
		7	3		4			2
7	2	5	6	1		4	9	
6	9		5		8		2	3
	4	3		7	2	1	5	6
4			1		7	9		
5			8				4	
	8			5	9	3		

Puzzle 8

Solution on 128

sudoku

★

		2	8		3	7	5	1
		7		2				
		8		7	5		6	9
2	7	4	3		1		9	8
3	8						1	2
6	5		2		9	3	4	7
7	2		9	6		1		
				1		9		
9	1	6	7		8	4		

Puzzle 9

Solution on 128

sudoku

★

2	6		5	9			8	
	1		2		8	6	3	
8						2	5	4
3	8				6		9	7
		6				1		
9	5		7				4	6
6	9	8						5
	3	7	4		1		6	
	2			6	5		7	8

Puzzle 10

Solution on 128

sudoku

☆

6	1		2					7
4	5		6	9				1
7	8				3	2	4	
1			7		9	5	2	
2				3				8
	3	7	5		2			9
	2	6	3				9	4
9				2	4		3	5
3					5		7	2

Puzzle 11

Solution on 128

sudoku

☆

3	4					9		
			9	1	2			8
1			8				5	
2	3	1	7		8	4	9	
9		4	2		3	7		1
	8	5	1		9	2	6	3
	9				6			4
4			5	9	1			
		6					3	9

Puzzle 12

Solution on 129

sudoku

☆

4	5	8		2	3		1	6
	2		4	5			9	
9				1				2
5		9	2			3		4
	4						7	
3		7			4	2		8
6				7				5
	8			4	9		2	
2	7		3	6		4	8	9

Puzzle 13

Solution on 129

sudoku

★

	5			9		2		4
4	9	8	3	6		7		
1	3	2	5					9
			4					6
8		3	2		6	9		5
6					3			
3					4	5	9	8
		4		8	9	1	6	3
9		1		3			7	

Puzzle 14

Solution on 129

sudoku

★

8				2		9		
			5	9			1	4
9		3						6
6	7	8		3	9	4	5	
1	3						7	9
	9	4	1	7		2	8	3
2						1		5
3	6			8	1			
		7		5				8

Puzzle 15

Solution on 129

sudoku

☆

1	5		6	7	9			
	6		8	1		7		5
7	3		2		5	6		1
6			1	2		3		
	1						5	
		7		5	6			2
5		6	9		2		4	3
9		3		6	1		2	
			4	3	7		6	9

Puzzle 16

Solution on 129

sudoku

☆

5	3	7	4			9		8
	1	2		7				
6	8				1	7	2	
3					4	8		7
	4		7		3		6	
8		5	6					4
	5	3	8				7	9
				9		2	5	
7		1			5	6	8	3

Puzzle 17

Solution on 129

sudoku

★

5		6		8		3		
	9		3		7			
4		3		6	5	7	9	8
				2	3	5		7
		4	5		1	8		
3		7	8	9				
7	3	2	9	4		1		5
			1		2		7	
		1		5		6		3

Puzzle 18

Solution on 130

sudoku

★

9	7			2	6	3	4	5
			5	7	4			
4			8	9				7
		1	6				7	4
	8						6	
7	2				5	8		
6				5	1			2
			3	4	8			
8	5	9	2	6			3	1

Puzzle 19

Solution on 130

sudoku

★

9	1	4	3			8		
				7	1	5		
3		7		8	2	6		1
	6					1		2
	9	1	6		5	3	7	
8		3					5	
5		9	2	1		4		3
		2	5	6				
		6			3	2	1	5

Puzzle 20

Solution on 130

sudoku

★

	9	6	1	2		7	3	5
						2		4
				9	3			
	1		3		6			7
7		4	9		2	1		6
2			8		7		4	
			4	7				
6		1						
4	2	7		8	5	3	1	

Puzzle 21

Solution on 130

sudoku

★

1	9	5	3		4	6	7	
	7		1				3	
		2		7			1	5
	3	6						7
		4	5	6	7	3		
7						1	4	
9	6			8		7		
	8				3		6	
	2	1	7		6	4	8	3

Puzzle 22

Solution on 130

sudoku

☆

	4		8		1	5	7	6
	2		5		7			
5					9	1		2
		9		8	6		4	
		1	2		4	9		
	8		9	7		6		
7		6	4					3
			6		8		1	
8	1	2	7		5		6	

Puzzle 23

Solution on 130

sudoku

☆

			7	4			5	2
	9		6		5		7	
	1	7	8		3	6		
		5			7	4		
9	7		4		1		8	5
		1	2			7		
		2	3		4	8	6	
	6		5		2		1	
7	3			8	6			

Puzzle 24

Solution on 131

sudoku

☆

				5	1	3	2	
1		3	2	4	6	5		
2	4		3		8			9
				3	4			
	5	1				4	8	
			5	8				
4			7		3		5	1
		7	4	2	9	8		3
	3	2	8	1				

Puzzle 25

Solution on 131

sudoku

★

7	3	9			8	1		
	1		6		7			
		5	9		1			3
1			2	5			9	
9		4	7		3	5		8
	7			9	4			2
6			3		9	2		
			4		2		7	
		7	1			6	3	9

Puzzle 26

Solution on 131

sudoku

★

2		6		8	9			
5		4		7			9	2
8	9				4			
4	5	7	8	6				1
9								6
1				9	2	5	7	8
			1				6	9
6	1			3		7		4
			9	4		1		3

Puzzle 27

Solution on 131

sudoku

★

	7	8			6			
4					1			6
6	2	1		8		4	7	5
	8		2		7	9		
7								1
		9	1		5		6	
8	5	4		1		6	3	2
3			8					7
			6			8	5	

Puzzle 28

Solution on 131

sudoku

★

	1				8	3	4	
	3		9					
	7		5	3				9
	2		4	5		7	9	
5	4		1		7		3	6
	8	7		2	9		5	
3				4	1		6	
					3		8	
	9	1	8				7	

Puzzle 29

Solution on 131

sudoku

☆

1		4	2		6			7
2		9		7				
6	8	7						5
8				9		7	1	
7	4			6			8	9
	9	1		8				2
3						9	2	8
				1		3		6
9			3		5	1		4

Puzzle 30

Solution on 132

sudoku

★★

		4		3			6	
8	9	6	7	2	1		4	
		1				7	8	
1					5	9		
		5	2		7	6		
		7	9					4
	7	8				2		
	2		6	7	4	8	3	1
	1			8		4		

Puzzle 31

Solution on 132

sudoku

★★

				5		8		
	6		7				1	3
	9		3		6		2	5
	2	4	8			5	7	9
	3	7				2	4	
5	8	9			4	1	3	
8	7		9		3		5	
9	5				7		8	
		6		8				

Puzzle 32

Solution on 132

sudoku

★★

	5	9			4			
2	1	4		9	8	7		5
	7	3	1				9	
		1					8	
		8	7		9	1		
	6					3		
	8				6	4	3	
4		5	8	1		6	2	9
			2			5	7	

Puzzle 33

Solution on 132

sudoku

★★

9	2		7	8	5	1		4
8		1			4			
			2			7		
1		8	4	6				
2	6	7				9	4	1
				7	2	6		5
		9			7			
			9			4		7
7		4	8	2	1		6	9

Puzzle 34

Solution on 132

sudoku

★★

	3			6	7			1
1	6	5	4	9			7	2
9					2			
	9	1	2					
7								5
					4	2	1	
			7					3
4	1			2	3	9	5	8
8			9	4			6	

Puzzle 35

Solution on 132

sudoku

★★

		7		8		9	6	
		9		4				1
		5			9	2	4	
4		6		9	7	8		2
			8		3			
9		8	4	2		5		6
	8	3	1			6		
2				7		4		
	9	4		3		1		

Puzzle 36

Solution on 133

sudoku

★★

	9						7	3
1		6	3	9				2
7	4		8					6
			5	3				7
9		8				1		4
5				4	9			
3					5		2	9
4				2	3	7		1
6	2						8	

Puzzle 37

Solution on 133

sudoku

★★

							8	1
	7		2	8	1	5	9	3
3			9		6			
7						4	5	
		5	8		7	9		
	4	2						7
			1		2			6
1	6	4	3	9	8		7	
2	8							

Puzzle 38

Solution on 133

sudoku

★★

9	8	1	4		5	3		7
				3			9	
					1	2		
1		8		9	4	6		3
				6				
6		4	7	1		9		2
		9	8					
	3			4				
8		7	3		6	4	1	9

Puzzle 39

Solution on 133

sudoku

★★

			2			3	4	7
1			3			2		6
		4					9	1
7			4	9				
		9	7		3	5		
				8	5			4
4	2					7		
8		7			4			2
9	6	3			2			

Puzzle 40

Solution on 133

sudoku

★★

	1		7			8		
7			6				9	
5		2			3		1	7
		1		8			5	9
8				6				3
3	9			2		4		
4	7		2			9		5
	2				5			6
		3			6		7	

Puzzle 41

Solution on 133

sudoku

★★

	3					8	1	2
1			3					9
	6			1		5	3	7
8				5	1	7		
	7			6			5	
		3	7	8				4
3	5	1		4			7	
4					5			1
6	8	2					4	

Puzzle 42

Solution on 134

sudoku

★★

	8					1		
2	6	7	8	1			4	5
	9					7		
			3	8		4	5	
		3	2		4	6		
	4	9		6	5			
		4					2	
1	7			5	8	3	6	4
		8					9	

Puzzle 43

Solution on 134

sudoku

★★

					7			8
	5	9	8		3		4	
		3				5	9	7
9	1		5					
	4			8			1	
					2		7	5
5	7	4				3		
	8		2		1	7	5	
1			3					

Puzzle 44

Solution on 134

sudoku

★★

	2		4			8		
	4			9		2	3	
1	8			3	5	4		
	9				7			
	3			1			7	
			6				2	
		4	3	6			5	2
	7	8		5			4	
		5			2		1	

Puzzle 45

Solution on 134

sudoku

★★

	8	7						
		5	1	7		8	2	
1				2	9			3
	1	4	3					8
		9		1		2		
7					8	6	4	
9			2	8				6
	7	8		4	3	9		
						3	8	

Puzzle 46

Solution on 134

sudoku

★★

6		5	7	1	2			4
				5				
	7					2	5	
5			1	2			8	
	6		5		9		1	
	2			6	4			7
	1	9					6	
				7				
8			9	3	5	7		1

Puzzle 47

Solution on 134

sudoku

★★

1					8		5	6
	3						1	
		9		2	4			
				7		2		
4	2		9		5		8	3
		3		4				
			6	3		5		
	5						6	
2	9		5					8

Puzzle 48

Solution on 135

sudoku

★★

				9	3	2		
5	4					8		
			5		1		6	
						6	3	2
	2		4		6		5	
1	5	6						
	6		1		7			
		1					8	9
		8	3	2				

Puzzle 49

Solution on 135

sudoku

	6	2	4					9
			8					6
	9		3			7	2	
				6			5	3
	3	4				6	9	
5	8			1				
	7	3			9		6	
4					7			
6					8	3	4	

Puzzle 50

Solution on 135

sudoku

★★

1		4			9		7	
				2	5			
	2				8	1		
5				3				2
2		1				4		3
3				1				9
		9	8				2	
			2	9				
	6		7			3		5

Puzzle 51

Solution on 135

sudoku

★★

		8				3	2	4
			4	6				
	9	4		7				
8			9		6		3	
7		9				4		1
	3		7		4			5
				8		2	4	
				5	9			
2	8	7				9		

Puzzle 52

Solution on 135

sudoku

★★

			6		2		8	
		6		8				4
	5				9		1	
3	6		8	5	4	7		1
		7				8		
8		1	2	6	7		4	5
	7		4				5	
1				7		2		
	3		1		6			

Puzzle 53

Solution on 135

sudoku

★★

					7		6	1
		4			1			
1				2	3	5		
2		5				1	3	
			8	5	2			
	4	9				2		8
		3	4	1				9
			2			3		
8	5		3					

Puzzle 54

Solution on 136

sudoku

★★

8	9							
			7		9			5
	2		3	1		6	8	
	1	6						
		4		2		7		
						2	3	
	8	9		3	2		4	
1			8		5			
							6	1

Puzzle 55

Solution on 136

sudoku

★★

	4		2		7			
	5		8					9
	9					1		3
4						2	1	
6			4		1			5
	1	9						7
9		4					5	
5					9		7	
			6		2		3	

Puzzle 56

Solution on 136

sudoku

★★

		9			8			
			2			9	5	6
3	2	4						
	6		3			4		9
	3			7			1	
4		7			2		6	
						6	4	7
2	7	8			3			
			1			3		

Puzzle 57

Solution on 136

sudoku

★★

1		2		5		7		
7								
	5		4	2		9		
					2		3	5
	1		6		8		7	
2	4		7					
		5		6	3		8	
								2
		6		7		3		1

Puzzle 58

Solution on 136

sudoku

★★

8		3						
9				8			3	7
	6			9	5			
		4	9			3	1	
5			4		8			2
	9	1			7	4		
			1	4			7	
4	7			2				1
						5		3

Puzzle 59

Solution on 136

sudoku

★★

	9	4	8					
	6					8	4	
					1	6		3
	8			1		7		4
3				7				8
4		7		8			1	
7		6	1					
	3	5					9	
					6	2	8	

Puzzle 60

Solution on 137

sudoku

★★★

			8		7			
		3					7	9
	7	8	2					
7	6			3			5	
3			4		5			8
	8			1			6	4
					9	5	2	
8	2					6		
			6		4			

Puzzle 61

Solution on 137

sudoku

★★★

	4	8			7			2
2					6	1		
	9		8		5			6
4					8		7	
		6				3		
	1		6					4
7			1		9		6	
		4	2					7
1			7			2	9	

Puzzle 62

Solution on 137

sudoku

★★★

9	5		8					
		8	1	2		4		
3			4				7	8
						5	4	6
	6			5			2	
8	3	5						
2	4				1			5
		6		3	4	2		
					2		1	4

Puzzle 63

Solution on 137

sudoku

★★★

		5						
					7	4		9
6			3			1	5	
7			1			5	9	
	1		6		8		2	
	5	6			9			4
	6	7			3			5
3		9	4					
						6		

Puzzle 64

Solution on 137

sudoku

★★★

		4			9	8		
8	5		7					6
				3		9	4	
						7	8	1
	7						2	
9	2	8						
	8	2		9				
5					1		7	2
		6	2			4		

Puzzle 65

Solution on 137

sudoku

★★★

2		3			5			
	4				3		6	8
				7	4	1		
1		5						9
	8						5	
4						6		7
		9	4	3				
7	5		6				3	
			5			7		6

Puzzle 66

Solution on 138

sudoku

★★★

	3		9					
2				8	3			
		1					4	6
		2		7				8
	8		1		2		6	
1				6		7		
3	5					9		
			7	3				2
					1		7	

Puzzle 67

Solution on 138

sudoku

★★★

5						2	4	
9	3					5		
					6	9		1
6				3	4			
	8						3	
			2	8				9
8		9	4					
		3					2	6
	4	7						5

Puzzle 68

Solution on 138

sudoku

★★★

7	8				5	1		
	1	5			6			3
		3				9		
	7						3	5
			5		9			
5	6						8	
		2				7		
4			9			5	1	
		6	7				9	8

Puzzle 69

Solution on 138

sudoku

★★★

	2			4				
9		1						6
		5	3				9	
5	1		6			4		
		9		3		5		
		4			5		6	8
	8				2	9		
2						7		4
				8			1	

Puzzle 70

Solution on 138

sudoku

★★★

9	6				7			
					9	4	5	
7				2	3			9
	3	4						
			5		2			
						3	9	
2			3	6				8
	7	9	2					
			9				3	1

Puzzle 71

Solution on 138

sudoku

★★★

			3		8			9
		7			1		5	
	8						3	1
6				3		1	9	
				1				
	2	5		6				4
9	3						6	
	4		6			9		
2			7		9			

Puzzle 72

Solution on 139

sudoku

★★★

5	6				2			
9							1	7
				9		5		
6			8			1		
7			2		3			6
		1			6			3
		5		2				
8	3							9
			5				7	8

Puzzle 73

Solution on 139

sudoku

★★★

	9					6		8
3					7			
	7				2			5
			9			7	1	
	2	9				8	3	
	1	8			3			
8			2				9	
			6					3
1		3					8	

Puzzle 74

Solution on 139

sudoku

★★★

		5			2			6
	3		5					
	6					2		7
9				1		5		
	2			9			7	
		3		7				1
1		6					4	
					6		8	
4			8			9		

Puzzle 75

Solution on 139

sudoku

★★★

				9		3		4
					5			
3	5	6					9	
4	8	3			2	7		
		9	7			5	1	8
	3					4	7	1
			3					
2		4		5				

Puzzle 76

Solution on 139

sudoku

★★★

		3			5	7		
7			1	6		5		
	8			3		4		
4	5		3				1	
	3				8		2	9
		4		1			5	
		8		5	4			3
		5	7			9		

Puzzle 77

Solution on 139

sudoku

★★★

3						8	2	
6				8	2			
		2	1			5	6	
	6			7				9
	9						5	
1				5			7	
	1	6			9	4		
			8	4				2
	4	9						8

Puzzle 78

Solution on 140

sudoku

★★★

3							7	8
		5	3		8			
		2			6			4
	3			4		9		
			5		1			
		6		3			1	
5			7			3		
			6		4	8		
2	7							5

Puzzle 79

Solution on 140

sudoku

★★★

			8					
						8	2	9
8	9	7			6	5		
6					4	9		
5	2			3			4	6
		4	7					2
		9	4			6	7	8
4	1	6						
					2			

Puzzle 80

Solution on 140

sudoku

★★★

			5	7	6	9		
2	5							
6						4	8	
						3		4
			1	3	8			
5		6						
	4	5						1
							3	7
		8	2	5	1			

Puzzle 81

Solution on 140

sudoku

★★★

			2		4			
		6				9		3
			9	5		1		
3	5	7					8	
	9			4			5	
	2					7	6	9
		9		2	1			
2		3				8		
			8		7			

Puzzle 82

Solution on 140

sudoku

★★★

				9			3	4
	1	2			5			
		5		6				2
	8				6	1		
		9				7		
		6	9				4	
7				5		2		
			4			3	6	
6	3			2				

Puzzle 83

Solution on 140

sudoku

★★★

	5		4				1	
		9						6
2	4			5		7		
3			5		7			
7		4				1		5
			8		4			2
		6		2			4	1
1						9		
	9				3		2	

Puzzle 84

Solution on 141

sudoku

★★★

			5		2			7
					1	6	2	
		6			7	4		
8	1			7			3	
	3						6	
	7			2			4	8
		3	7			8		
	5	1	2					
2			3		5			

Puzzle 85

Solution on 141

sudoku

★★★

		9	4		3			
	6							5
		5	6			8	3	
	5			4		3		
1				7				6
		7		8			9	
	9	3			7	6		
7							1	
			5		2	7		

Puzzle 86

Solution on 141

sudoku

★★★

2								9
		7	5		1			
					3	4	5	
		8		5			2	1
	1						7	
3	2			1		6		
	7	5	9					
			4		5	3		
9								2

Puzzle 87

Solution on 141

sudoku

★★★

3		1		5			6	
		9						5
		6		9	2			
5	4				9		1	
				3				
	2		5				9	8
			9	4		8		
8						1		
	3			1		7		4

Puzzle 88

Solution on 141

sudoku

★★★

9			5					
8	3							
		2	7				3	4
		3		4	5			
	5	4				1	9	
			9	1		2		
3	8				6	4		
							5	7
					8			6

Puzzle 89

Solution on 141

sudoku

★★★

	7					4		6
			1				8	
	5		6	7				3
2	1							
		7	8		9	2		
							6	7
6				8	1		4	
	8				2			
9		2					7	

Puzzle 90

Solution on 142

sudoku

★★★★

7	5		1					
9				4	6			
					8	9	1	
		3				2		9
6		1				4		
	8	6	4					
			6	5				7
					1		5	4

Puzzle 91

Solution on 142

sudoku

★★★★

	4				3	9		
	8		1					3
	9		8		7			
		7		8		6	9	
8								7
	6	9		7		4		
			6		4		5	
4					8		1	
		1	9				6	

Puzzle 92

Solution on 142

sudoku

★★★★

					7	8	9	2
7								
		9		2	4	5		
4		2			3			8
			2		9			
9			7			1		4
		5	1	8		4		
								5
2	1	7	4					

Puzzle 93

Solution on 142

sudoku

★★★★

	8		3					
	7		5	1		8		
		6				1	2	
7			9	3				2
9								6
3				7	2			1
	3	5				2		
		1		4	5		7	
					3		4	

Puzzle 94

Solution on 142

sudoku

★★★★

8			7					
	6				9		2	
			1	5		7	8	
		4				6		
6		2		3		9		4
		8				2		
	7	6		4	5			
	2		9				4	
					2			1

Puzzle 95

Solution on 142

sudoku

★★★★

			4		7			
		3	6					7
	5	7				6		9
5				3			4	
	9						3	
	6			9				2
6		9				5	2	
7					8	3		
			9		2			

Puzzle 96

Solution on 143

sudoku

★★★★

	8			9	3			
			8				9	
6	7			4				
		4	9			2	8	
		2				6		
	3	5			8	9		
				6			4	7
	2				4			
			1	8			6	

Puzzle 97

Solution on 143

sudoku

★★★★

						6		9
			5	8				
8	9		2			4		
3	4					7		
		6	8		2	3		
		8					6	2
		9			3		1	5
				7	8			
6		3						

Puzzle 98

Solution on 143

sudoku

★★★★

	9							6
		3		7	6			
	7		5				9	
			4			9	6	1
9								5
2	6	8			9			
	4				7		5	
			6	4		7		
5							8	

Puzzle 99

Solution on 143

sudoku

★★★★

				3		6		8
2	8		5					
			7			9		
3	6	7		5				
		1				4		
				8		7	9	6
		2			1			
					5		7	1
6		5		2				

Puzzle 100

Solution on 143

sudoku

★★★★

	5		4	6				1
		1	2				5	
7						9		4
	7		5	3		8		
3								5
		6		9	4		3	
4		2						8
	3				2	5		
8				4	3		7	

Puzzle 101

Solution on 143

sudoku

★★★★

			8					1
		1	3				4	6
		7			5			2
				3	4	8		
	2						3	
		5	6	8				
2			7			9		
6	9				2	4		
7					3			

Puzzle 102

Solution on 144

sudoku

★★★★

1					6			
	3	4			5			
	6				4	8	1	
6		8						7
	4						9	
3						2		8
	2	3	9				5	
			1			9	2	
			2					4

Puzzle 103

Solution on 144

sudoku

★★★★

	5	3					6	
6			1			2	8	
				6		9		
7				5	3			8
2			8	4				1
		5		9				
	8	6			2			3
	2					4	1	

Puzzle 104

Solution on 144

sudoku

★★★★

6					9	1		
					5			3
	1		2			5		
5	6					4		1
			9		2			
9		3					7	8
		5			4		3	
2			6					
		6	5					7

Puzzle 105

Solution on 144

sudoku

★★★★

		2		6		4		
	4					9		
6			3			5		
5					6		2	
			5		3			
	2		9					8
		3			2			6
		8					9	
		1		4		8		

Puzzle 106

Solution on 144

sudoku

★★★★

				4	5			
	4					2		3
	7		3			1	6	
		7			9			2
1								5
2			1			8		
	8	5			7		9	
6		1					2	
			5	1				

Puzzle 107

Solution on 144

sudoku

★★★★

	4			5	2			
			1					6
						9	4	1
		3			4		9	
7		4				5		3
	1		7			4		
9	6	7						
8					6			
			2	8			3	

Puzzle 108

Solution on 145

sudoku

★★★★

6				8			7	
1			2				4	
		9	4			5		
	9				8			5
		5				6		
8			6				1	
		8			2	9		
	7				1			4
	3			5				7

Puzzle 109

Solution on 145

sudoku

★★★★

			9					
	6				4	8		2
	4	1	5					7
						2	5	
	7						8	
	1	6						
6					8	5	3	
9		8	2				7	
					6			

Puzzle 110

Solution on 145

sudoku

★★★★

	6			5		3		
						4		
2			6	8	4			
			5			7		1
7	9						8	6
1		5			8			
			4	9	1			5
		4						
		1		7			2	

Puzzle 111

Solution on 145

sudoku

★★★★

	7			9		6		
5		2	3					
	8					5		3
	3	9						7
			4		6			
2						8	5	
9		3					7	
					8	9		5
		8		1			2	

Puzzle 112

Solution on 145

sudoku

★★★★

		7					6	
				4	2		3	
2				3			1	
3	2					9		
			8		1			
		9					8	6
	6			8				3
	9		5	2				
	8					5		

Puzzle 113

Solution on 145

sudoku

★★★★

	1				3			2
							4	
	2			6	9			3
5			3	2			9	
		8				2		
	9			4	1			8
6			5	8			7	
	8							
3			9				2	

Puzzle 114

Solution on 146

sudoku

★★★★

		7				6		9
	5		7					
4				3				
					9		8	6
	2		6		4		5	
8	4		5					
				1				2
					5		1	
7		9				8		

Puzzle 115

Solution on 146

sudoku

★★★★

3			6				2	
					1		9	7
		8	9					
							7	4
9				1				8
6	5							
					8	4		
5	1		3					
	2				9			5

Puzzle 116

Solution on 146

sudoku

★★★★

1		4					6	
			2				8	
6			1					
		7	3		4	2		
2								9
		6	7		9	3		
					7			4
	9				6			
	5					6		3

Puzzle 117

Solution on 146

Answers

Puzzle 1

8	4	3	1	5	6	7	2	9
1	2	6	9	3	7	5	4	8
7	9	5	8	4	2	3	1	6
9	5	8	6	7	4	1	3	2
3	7	1	2	9	8	4	6	5
4	6	2	3	1	5	9	8	7
6	1	7	5	8	3	2	9	4
5	8	9	4	2	1	6	7	3
2	3	4	7	6	9	8	5	1

Puzzle 2

2	9	1	3	4	6	5	7	8
6	7	8	5	2	9	1	3	4
3	5	4	7	1	8	2	9	6
4	3	7	9	6	5	8	1	2
1	6	2	8	7	4	9	5	3
5	8	9	1	3	2	4	6	7
7	4	3	2	9	1	6	8	5
8	1	6	4	5	3	7	2	9
9	2	5	6	8	7	3	4	1

Puzzle 3

9	6	7	5	1	2	3	8	4
8	3	1	6	9	4	2	5	7
4	2	5	7	8	3	6	9	1
7	4	9	1	5	6	8	2	3
3	8	6	9	2	7	4	1	5
1	5	2	4	3	8	9	7	6
6	9	3	8	7	1	5	4	2
2	7	8	3	4	5	1	6	9
5	1	4	2	6	9	7	3	8

Puzzle 4

2	5	3	7	6	8	4	9	1
6	7	4	9	5	1	2	8	3
9	1	8	2	4	3	6	7	5
7	2	9	3	8	4	5	1	6
1	8	6	5	9	2	7	3	4
3	4	5	1	7	6	8	2	9
8	3	2	4	1	5	9	6	7
5	9	1	6	2	7	3	4	8
4	6	7	8	3	9	1	5	2

Puzzle 5

1	4	2	6	7	5	8	9	3
7	5	8	9	1	3	6	2	4
6	3	9	2	8	4	5	1	7
9	6	4	7	3	1	2	8	5
2	7	1	8	5	6	3	4	9
3	8	5	4	9	2	7	6	1
4	9	6	3	2	7	1	5	8
5	2	7	1	4	8	9	3	6
8	1	3	5	6	9	4	7	2

Puzzle 6

8	6	9	5	7	2	1	4	3
5	7	4	6	1	3	8	2	9
1	3	2	8	9	4	7	6	5
4	8	3	9	5	7	6	1	2
7	5	1	2	3	6	4	9	8
9	2	6	1	4	8	3	5	7
3	1	5	4	8	9	2	7	6
2	4	8	7	6	5	9	3	1
6	9	7	3	2	1	5	8	4

Puzzle 7

9	2	6	4	3	7	5	1	8
8	7	3	2	1	5	6	9	4
4	1	5	6	8	9	3	2	7
2	8	9	3	5	4	7	6	1
6	3	1	9	7	2	8	4	5
5	4	7	8	6	1	9	3	2
1	6	4	7	9	8	2	5	3
3	5	8	1	2	6	4	7	9
7	9	2	5	4	3	1	8	6

Puzzle 8

3	1	4	2	6	5	8	7	9
2	5	8	7	9	1	6	3	4
9	6	7	3	8	4	5	1	2
7	2	5	6	1	3	4	9	8
6	9	1	5	4	8	7	2	3
8	4	3	9	7	2	1	5	6
4	3	6	1	2	7	9	8	5
5	7	9	8	3	6	2	4	1
1	8	2	4	5	9	3	6	7

Puzzle 9

4	6	2	8	9	3	7	5	1
5	9	7	1	2	6	8	3	4
1	3	8	4	7	5	2	6	9
2	7	4	3	5	1	6	9	8
3	8	9	6	4	7	5	1	2
6	5	1	2	8	9	3	4	7
7	2	5	9	6	4	1	8	3
8	4	3	5	1	2	9	7	6
9	1	6	7	3	8	4	2	5

Puzzle 10

2	6	3	5	9	4	7	8	1
4	1	5	2	7	8	6	3	9
8	7	9	6	1	3	2	5	4
3	8	2	1	4	6	5	9	7
7	4	6	8	5	9	1	2	3
9	5	1	7	3	2	8	4	6
6	9	8	3	2	7	4	1	5
5	3	7	4	8	1	9	6	2
1	2	4	9	6	5	3	7	8

Puzzle 11

6	1	3	2	4	8	9	5	7
4	5	2	6	9	7	3	8	1
7	8	9	1	5	3	2	4	6
1	6	4	7	8	9	5	2	3
2	9	5	4	3	6	7	1	8
8	3	7	5	1	2	4	6	9
5	2	6	3	7	1	8	9	4
9	7	1	8	2	4	6	3	5
3	4	8	9	6	5	1	7	2

Puzzle 12

3	4	8	6	7	5	9	1	2
6	5	7	9	1	2	3	4	8
1	2	9	8	3	4	6	5	7
2	3	1	7	6	8	4	9	5
9	6	4	2	5	3	7	8	1
7	8	5	1	4	9	2	6	3
5	9	2	3	8	6	1	7	4
4	7	3	5	9	1	8	2	6
8	1	6	4	2	7	5	3	9

Puzzle 13

4	5	8	9	2	3	7	1	6
7	2	1	4	5	6	8	9	3
9	3	6	7	1	8	5	4	2
5	1	9	2	8	7	3	6	4
8	4	2	6	3	5	9	7	1
3	6	7	1	9	4	2	5	8
6	9	4	8	7	2	1	3	5
1	8	3	5	4	9	6	2	7
2	7	5	3	6	1	4	8	9

Puzzle 14

7	5	6	8	9	1	2	3	4
4	9	8	3	6	2	7	5	1
1	3	2	5	4	7	6	8	9
2	7	9	4	5	8	3	1	6
8	1	3	2	7	6	9	4	5
6	4	5	9	1	3	8	2	7
3	6	7	1	2	4	5	9	8
5	2	4	7	8	9	1	6	3
9	8	1	6	3	5	4	7	2

Puzzle 15

8	5	1	6	2	4	9	3	7
7	2	6	5	9	3	8	1	4
9	4	3	7	1	8	5	2	6
6	7	8	2	3	9	4	5	1
1	3	2	8	4	5	6	7	9
5	9	4	1	7	6	2	8	3
2	8	9	3	6	7	1	4	5
3	6	5	4	8	1	7	9	2
4	1	7	9	5	2	3	6	8

Puzzle 16

1	5	8	6	7	9	2	3	4
2	6	4	8	1	3	7	9	5
7	3	9	2	4	5	6	8	1
6	9	5	1	2	4	3	7	8
3	1	2	7	9	8	4	5	6
4	8	7	3	5	6	9	1	2
5	7	6	9	8	2	1	4	3
9	4	3	5	6	1	8	2	7
8	2	1	4	3	7	5	6	9

Puzzle 17

5	3	7	4	6	2	9	1	8
9	1	2	5	7	8	3	4	6
6	8	4	9	3	1	7	2	5
3	2	6	1	5	4	8	9	7
1	4	9	7	8	3	5	6	2
8	7	5	6	2	9	1	3	4
2	5	3	8	1	6	4	7	9
4	6	8	3	9	7	2	5	1
7	9	1	2	4	5	6	8	3

Puzzle 18

5	7	6	4	8	9	3	1	2
2	9	8	3	1	7	4	5	6
4	1	3	2	6	5	7	9	8
1	8	9	6	2	3	5	4	7
6	2	4	5	7	1	8	3	9
3	5	7	8	9	4	2	6	1
7	3	2	9	4	6	1	8	5
8	6	5	1	3	2	9	7	4
9	4	1	7	5	8	6	2	3

Puzzle 19

9	7	8	1	2	6	3	4	5
1	3	2	5	7	4	6	9	8
4	6	5	8	9	3	1	2	7
3	9	1	6	8	2	5	7	4
5	8	4	7	1	9	2	6	3
7	2	6	4	3	5	8	1	9
6	4	3	9	5	1	7	8	2
2	1	7	3	4	8	9	5	6
8	5	9	2	6	7	4	3	1

Puzzle 20

9	1	4	3	5	6	8	2	7
6	2	8	9	7	1	5	3	4
3	5	7	4	8	2	6	9	1
7	6	5	8	3	9	1	4	2
2	9	1	6	4	5	3	7	8
8	4	3	1	2	7	9	5	6
5	7	9	2	1	8	4	6	3
1	3	2	5	6	4	7	8	9
4	8	6	7	9	3	2	1	5

Puzzle 21

8	9	6	1	2	4	7	3	5
1	7	3	5	6	8	2	9	4
5	4	2	7	9	3	8	6	1
9	1	8	3	4	6	5	2	7
7	3	4	9	5	2	1	8	6
2	6	5	8	1	7	9	4	3
3	8	9	4	7	1	6	5	2
6	5	1	2	3	9	4	7	8
4	2	7	6	8	5	3	1	9

Puzzle 22

1	9	5	3	2	4	6	7	8
6	7	8	1	5	9	2	3	4
3	4	2	6	7	8	9	1	5
2	3	6	9	4	1	8	5	7
8	1	4	5	6	7	3	9	2
7	5	9	8	3	2	1	4	6
9	6	3	4	8	5	7	2	1
4	8	7	2	1	3	5	6	9
5	2	1	7	9	6	4	8	3

Puzzle 23

9	4	3	8	2	1	5	7	6
1	2	8	5	6	7	3	9	4
5	6	7	3	4	9	1	8	2
2	3	9	1	8	6	7	4	5
6	7	1	2	5	4	9	3	8
4	8	5	9	7	3	6	2	1
7	9	6	4	1	2	8	5	3
3	5	4	6	9	8	2	1	7
8	1	2	7	3	5	4	6	9

Puzzle 24

6	8	3	7	4	9	1	5	2
2	9	4	6	1	5	3	7	8
5	1	7	8	2	3	6	4	9
8	2	5	9	6	7	4	3	1
9	7	6	4	3	1	2	8	5
3	4	1	2	5	8	7	9	6
1	5	2	3	9	4	8	6	7
4	6	8	5	7	2	9	1	3
7	3	9	1	8	6	5	2	4

Puzzle 25

7	6	8	9	5	1	3	2	4
1	9	3	2	4	6	5	7	8
2	4	5	3	7	8	6	1	9
8	2	6	1	3	4	7	9	5
3	5	1	6	9	7	4	8	2
9	7	4	5	8	2	1	3	6
4	8	9	7	6	3	2	5	1
5	1	7	4	2	9	8	6	3
6	3	2	8	1	5	9	4	7

Puzzle 26

7	3	9	5	4	8	1	2	6
8	1	2	6	3	7	9	5	4
4	6	5	9	2	1	7	8	3
1	8	3	2	5	6	4	9	7
9	2	4	7	1	3	5	6	8
5	7	6	8	9	4	3	1	2
6	5	8	3	7	9	2	4	1
3	9	1	4	6	2	8	7	5
2	4	7	1	8	5	6	3	9

Puzzle 27

2	7	6	3	8	9	4	1	5
5	3	4	6	7	1	8	9	2
8	9	1	5	2	4	6	3	7
4	5	7	8	6	3	9	2	1
9	8	2	7	1	5	3	4	6
1	6	3	4	9	2	5	7	8
3	4	8	1	5	7	2	6	9
6	1	9	2	3	8	7	5	4
7	2	5	9	4	6	1	8	3

Puzzle 28

5	7	8	4	2	6	3	1	9
4	9	3	5	7	1	2	8	6
6	2	1	9	8	3	4	7	5
1	8	5	2	6	7	9	4	3
7	4	6	3	9	8	5	2	1
2	3	9	1	4	5	7	6	8
8	5	4	7	1	9	6	3	2
3	6	2	8	5	4	1	9	7
9	1	7	6	3	2	8	5	4

Puzzle 29

9	1	2	6	7	8	3	4	5
8	3	5	9	1	4	6	2	7
4	7	6	5	3	2	8	1	9
1	2	3	4	5	6	7	9	8
5	4	9	1	8	7	2	3	6
6	8	7	3	2	9	1	5	4
3	5	8	7	4	1	9	6	2
7	6	4	2	9	3	5	8	1
2	9	1	8	6	5	4	7	3

Puzzle 30

1	3	4	2	5	6	8	9	7
2	5	9	4	7	8	6	3	1
6	8	7	9	3	1	2	4	5
8	2	6	5	9	4	7	1	3
7	4	3	1	6	2	5	8	9
5	9	1	7	8	3	4	6	2
3	1	5	6	4	7	9	2	8
4	7	2	8	1	9	3	5	6
9	6	8	3	2	5	1	7	4

Puzzle 31

7	5	4	8	3	9	1	6	2
8	9	6	7	2	1	3	4	5
2	3	1	4	5	6	7	8	9
1	4	2	3	6	5	9	7	8
9	8	5	2	4	7	6	1	3
3	6	7	9	1	8	5	2	4
4	7	8	1	9	3	2	5	6
5	2	9	6	7	4	8	3	1
6	1	3	5	8	2	4	9	7

Puzzle 32

2	1	3	4	5	9	8	6	7
4	6	5	7	2	8	9	1	3
7	9	8	3	1	6	4	2	5
6	2	4	8	3	1	5	7	9
1	3	7	6	9	5	2	4	8
5	8	9	2	7	4	1	3	6
8	7	1	9	4	3	6	5	2
9	5	2	1	6	7	3	8	4
3	4	6	5	8	2	7	9	1

Puzzle 33

8	5	9	6	7	4	2	1	3
2	1	4	3	9	8	7	6	5
6	7	3	1	2	5	8	9	4
3	4	1	5	6	2	9	8	7
5	2	8	7	3	9	1	4	6
9	6	7	4	8	1	3	5	2
7	8	2	9	5	6	4	3	1
4	3	5	8	1	7	6	2	9
1	9	6	2	4	3	5	7	8

Puzzle 34

9	2	6	7	8	5	1	3	4
8	7	1	3	9	4	2	5	6
3	4	5	2	1	6	7	9	8
1	5	8	4	6	9	3	7	2
2	6	7	5	3	8	9	4	1
4	9	3	1	7	2	6	8	5
5	1	9	6	4	7	8	2	3
6	8	2	9	5	3	4	1	7
7	3	4	8	2	1	5	6	9

Puzzle 35

2	3	4	5	6	7	8	9	1
1	6	5	4	9	8	3	7	2
9	7	8	1	3	2	5	4	6
3	9	1	2	5	6	7	8	4
7	4	2	8	1	9	6	3	5
5	8	6	3	7	4	2	1	9
6	5	9	7	8	1	4	2	3
4	1	7	6	2	3	9	5	8
8	2	3	9	4	5	1	6	7

Puzzle 36

1	4	7	3	8	2	9	6	5
8	2	9	6	4	5	3	7	1
3	6	5	7	1	9	2	4	8
4	3	6	5	9	7	8	1	2
5	1	2	8	6	3	7	9	4
9	7	8	4	2	1	5	3	6
7	8	3	1	5	4	6	2	9
2	5	1	9	7	6	4	8	3
6	9	4	2	3	8	1	5	7

Puzzle 37

8	9	2	4	6	1	5	7	3
1	5	6	3	9	7	8	4	2
7	4	3	8	5	2	9	1	6
2	1	4	5	3	8	6	9	7
9	3	8	2	7	6	1	5	4
5	6	7	1	4	9	2	3	8
3	7	1	6	8	5	4	2	9
4	8	5	9	2	3	7	6	1
6	2	9	7	1	4	3	8	5

Puzzle 38

5	2	9	7	3	4	6	8	1
4	7	6	2	8	1	5	9	3
3	1	8	9	5	6	7	2	4
7	9	1	6	2	3	4	5	8
6	3	5	8	4	7	9	1	2
8	4	2	5	1	9	3	6	7
9	5	3	1	7	2	8	4	6
1	6	4	3	9	8	2	7	5
2	8	7	4	6	5	1	3	9

Puzzle 39

9	8	1	4	2	5	3	6	7
2	4	5	6	3	7	8	9	1
7	6	3	9	8	1	2	4	5
1	7	8	2	9	4	6	5	3
3	9	2	5	6	8	1	7	4
6	5	4	7	1	3	9	8	2
4	1	9	8	7	2	5	3	6
5	3	6	1	4	9	7	2	8
8	2	7	3	5	6	4	1	9

Puzzle 40

5	9	6	2	1	8	3	4	7
1	7	8	3	4	9	2	5	6
2	3	4	5	6	7	8	9	1
7	8	5	4	9	1	6	2	3
6	4	9	7	2	3	5	1	8
3	1	2	6	8	5	9	7	4
4	2	1	8	5	6	7	3	9
8	5	7	9	3	4	1	6	2
9	6	3	1	7	2	4	8	5

Puzzle 41

6	1	9	7	5	2	8	3	4
7	3	4	6	1	8	5	9	2
5	8	2	4	9	3	6	1	7
2	6	1	3	8	4	7	5	9
8	4	7	5	6	9	1	2	3
3	9	5	1	2	7	4	6	8
4	7	6	2	3	1	9	8	5
1	2	8	9	7	5	3	4	6
9	5	3	8	4	6	2	7	1

Puzzle 42

7	3	4	5	9	6	8	1	2
1	2	5	3	7	8	4	6	9
9	6	8	2	1	4	5	3	7
8	4	6	9	5	1	7	2	3
2	7	9	4	6	3	1	5	8
5	1	3	7	8	2	6	9	4
3	5	1	8	4	9	2	7	6
4	9	7	6	2	5	3	8	1
6	8	2	1	3	7	9	4	5

Puzzle 43

4	8	5	6	7	9	1	3	2
2	6	7	8	1	3	9	4	5
3	9	1	5	4	2	7	8	6
7	2	6	3	8	1	4	5	9
5	1	3	2	9	4	6	7	8
8	4	9	7	6	5	2	1	3
9	5	4	1	3	6	8	2	7
1	7	2	9	5	8	3	6	4
6	3	8	4	2	7	5	9	1

Puzzle 44

4	6	1	9	5	7	2	3	8
7	5	9	8	2	3	1	4	6
8	2	3	1	6	4	5	9	7
9	1	7	5	3	6	4	8	2
2	4	5	7	8	9	6	1	3
6	3	8	4	1	2	9	7	5
5	7	4	6	9	8	3	2	1
3	8	6	2	4	1	7	5	9
1	9	2	3	7	5	8	6	4

Puzzle 45

5	2	3	4	7	6	8	9	1
7	4	6	8	9	1	2	3	5
1	8	9	2	3	5	4	6	7
6	9	1	5	2	7	3	8	4
8	3	2	9	1	4	5	7	6
4	5	7	6	8	3	1	2	9
9	1	4	3	6	8	7	5	2
2	7	8	1	5	9	6	4	3
3	6	5	7	4	2	9	1	8

Puzzle 46

2	8	7	4	3	5	1	6	9
3	9	5	1	7	6	8	2	4
1	4	6	8	2	9	5	7	3
5	1	4	3	6	2	7	9	8
8	6	9	7	1	4	2	3	5
7	2	3	9	5	8	6	4	1
9	3	1	2	8	7	4	5	6
6	7	8	5	4	3	9	1	2
4	5	2	6	9	1	3	8	7

Puzzle 47

6	8	5	7	1	2	9	3	4
9	3	2	4	5	6	1	7	8
4	7	1	8	9	3	2	5	6
5	9	4	1	2	7	6	8	3
3	6	7	5	8	9	4	1	2
1	2	8	3	6	4	5	9	7
7	1	9	2	4	8	3	6	5
2	5	3	6	7	1	8	4	9
8	4	6	9	3	5	7	2	1

Puzzle 48

1	7	2	3	9	8	4	5	6
8	3	4	7	5	6	9	1	2
5	6	9	1	2	4	8	3	7
6	1	5	8	7	3	2	9	4
4	2	7	9	6	5	1	8	3
9	8	3	2	4	1	6	7	5
7	4	8	6	3	9	5	2	1
3	5	1	4	8	2	7	6	9
2	9	6	5	1	7	3	4	8

Puzzle 49

6	1	7	8	9	3	2	4	5
5	4	3	7	6	2	8	9	1
8	9	2	5	4	1	3	6	7
7	8	4	9	1	5	6	3	2
3	2	9	4	7	6	1	5	8
1	5	6	2	3	8	9	7	4
9	6	5	1	8	7	4	2	3
2	3	1	6	5	4	7	8	9
4	7	8	3	2	9	5	1	6

Puzzle 50

3	6	2	4	7	1	5	8	9
7	4	5	8	9	2	1	3	6
8	9	1	3	5	6	7	2	4
9	1	7	2	6	4	8	5	3
2	3	4	7	8	5	6	9	1
5	8	6	9	1	3	4	7	2
1	7	3	5	4	9	2	6	8
4	2	8	6	3	7	9	1	5
6	5	9	1	2	8	3	4	7

Puzzle 51

1	5	4	3	6	9	2	7	8
6	7	8	1	2	5	9	3	4
9	2	3	4	7	8	1	5	6
5	8	6	9	3	4	7	1	2
2	9	1	5	8	7	4	6	3
3	4	7	6	1	2	5	8	9
4	1	9	8	5	3	6	2	7
7	3	5	2	9	6	8	4	1
8	6	2	7	4	1	3	9	5

Puzzle 52

6	7	8	5	9	1	3	2	4
3	1	2	4	6	8	5	7	9
5	9	4	3	7	2	6	1	8
8	4	5	9	1	6	7	3	2
7	2	9	8	3	5	4	6	1
1	3	6	7	2	4	8	9	5
9	5	1	6	8	7	2	4	3
4	6	3	2	5	9	1	8	7
2	8	7	1	4	3	9	5	6

Puzzle 53

9	1	3	6	4	2	5	8	7
7	2	6	5	8	1	9	3	4
4	5	8	7	3	9	6	1	2
3	6	2	8	5	4	7	9	1
5	4	7	9	1	3	8	2	6
8	9	1	2	6	7	3	4	5
6	7	9	4	2	8	1	5	3
1	8	4	3	7	5	2	6	9
2	3	5	1	9	6	4	7	8

Puzzle 54

9	3	2	5	4	7	8	6	1
5	7	4	6	8	1	9	2	3
1	6	8	9	2	3	5	7	4
2	8	5	7	9	4	1	3	6
3	1	6	8	5	2	4	9	7
7	4	9	1	3	6	2	5	8
6	2	3	4	1	5	7	8	9
4	9	7	2	6	8	3	1	5
8	5	1	3	7	9	6	4	2

Puzzle 55

8	9	1	2	5	6	4	7	3
4	6	3	7	8	9	1	2	5
7	2	5	3	1	4	6	8	9
2	1	6	4	7	3	9	5	8
9	3	4	5	2	8	7	1	6
5	7	8	6	9	1	2	3	4
6	8	9	1	3	2	5	4	7
1	4	7	8	6	5	3	9	2
3	5	2	9	4	7	8	6	1

Puzzle 56

3	4	1	2	9	7	5	8	6
2	5	6	8	1	3	7	4	9
7	9	8	5	6	4	1	2	3
4	3	5	9	7	6	2	1	8
6	7	2	4	8	1	3	9	5
8	1	9	3	2	5	4	6	7
9	2	4	7	3	8	6	5	1
5	6	3	1	4	9	8	7	2
1	8	7	6	5	2	9	3	4

Puzzle 57

6	5	9	7	1	8	2	3	4
7	8	1	2	3	4	9	5	6
3	2	4	5	6	9	7	8	1
8	6	2	3	5	1	4	7	9
9	3	5	4	7	6	8	1	2
4	1	7	9	8	2	5	6	3
1	9	3	8	2	5	6	4	7
2	7	8	6	4	3	1	9	5
5	4	6	1	9	7	3	2	8

Puzzle 58

1	9	2	3	5	6	7	4	8
7	3	4	8	9	1	5	2	6
6	5	8	4	2	7	9	1	3
8	6	7	9	4	2	1	3	5
5	1	9	6	3	8	2	7	4
2	4	3	7	1	5	8	6	9
9	2	5	1	6	3	4	8	7
3	7	1	5	8	4	6	9	2
4	8	6	2	7	9	3	5	1

Puzzle 59

8	2	3	7	6	4	1	5	9
9	4	5	2	8	1	6	3	7
1	6	7	3	9	5	8	2	4
7	8	4	9	5	2	3	1	6
5	3	6	4	1	8	7	9	2
2	9	1	6	3	7	4	8	5
3	5	9	1	4	6	2	7	8
4	7	8	5	2	3	9	6	1
6	1	2	8	7	9	5	4	3

Puzzle 60

2	9	4	8	6	3	5	7	1
1	6	3	2	5	7	8	4	9
5	7	8	9	4	1	6	2	3
6	8	9	3	1	2	7	5	4
3	1	2	4	7	5	9	6	8
4	5	7	6	8	9	3	1	2
7	2	6	1	9	8	4	3	5
8	3	5	7	2	4	1	9	6
9	4	1	5	3	6	2	8	7

Puzzle 61

4	9	1	8	5	7	2	3	6
2	5	3	1	4	6	8	7	9
6	7	8	2	9	3	4	1	5
7	6	4	9	3	8	1	5	2
3	1	2	4	6	5	7	9	8
9	8	5	7	1	2	3	6	4
1	4	6	3	8	9	5	2	7
8	2	9	5	7	1	6	4	3
5	3	7	6	2	4	9	8	1

Puzzle 62

6	4	8	9	1	7	5	3	2
2	5	7	3	4	6	1	8	9
3	9	1	8	2	5	7	4	6
4	2	9	5	3	8	6	7	1
5	7	6	4	9	1	3	2	8
8	1	3	6	7	2	9	5	4
7	3	2	1	8	9	4	6	5
9	6	4	2	5	3	8	1	7
1	8	5	7	6	4	2	9	3

Puzzle 63

9	5	4	8	6	7	1	3	2
6	7	8	1	2	3	4	5	9
3	1	2	4	9	5	6	7	8
7	2	9	3	1	8	5	4	6
4	6	1	7	5	9	8	2	3
8	3	5	2	4	6	7	9	1
2	4	7	9	8	1	3	6	5
1	9	6	5	3	4	2	8	7
5	8	3	6	7	2	9	1	4

Puzzle 64

4	9	5	8	1	6	2	7	3
8	3	1	5	2	7	4	6	9
6	7	2	3	9	4	1	5	8
7	8	3	1	4	2	5	9	6
9	1	4	6	5	8	3	2	7
2	5	6	7	3	9	8	1	4
1	6	7	2	8	3	9	4	5
3	2	9	4	6	5	7	8	1
5	4	8	9	7	1	6	3	2

Puzzle 65

2	3	4	5	6	9	8	1	7
8	5	9	7	1	4	2	3	6
1	6	7	8	3	2	9	4	5
3	4	5	9	2	6	7	8	1
6	7	1	3	4	8	5	2	9
9	2	8	1	7	5	3	6	4
4	8	2	6	9	7	1	5	3
5	9	3	4	8	1	6	7	2
7	1	6	2	5	3	4	9	8

Puzzle 66

2	1	3	8	6	5	9	7	4
9	4	7	1	2	3	5	6	8
5	6	8	9	7	4	1	2	3
1	7	5	2	8	6	3	4	9
3	8	6	7	4	9	2	5	1
4	9	2	3	5	1	6	8	7
6	2	9	4	3	7	8	1	5
7	5	1	6	9	8	4	3	2
8	3	4	5	1	2	7	9	6

Puzzle 67

5	3	6	9	1	4	2	8	7
2	7	4	6	8	3	5	9	1
8	9	1	2	5	7	3	4	6
9	6	2	4	7	5	1	3	8
7	8	3	1	9	2	4	6	5
1	4	5	3	6	8	7	2	9
3	5	7	8	2	6	9	1	4
4	1	8	7	3	9	6	5	2
6	2	9	5	4	1	8	7	3

Puzzle 68

5	7	6	8	9	1	2	4	3
9	3	1	7	4	2	5	6	8
4	2	8	3	5	6	9	7	1
6	9	5	1	3	4	7	8	2
7	8	2	5	6	9	1	3	4
3	1	4	2	8	7	6	5	9
8	6	9	4	2	5	3	1	7
1	5	3	9	7	8	4	2	6
2	4	7	6	1	3	8	9	5

Puzzle 69

7	8	4	3	9	5	1	2	6
9	1	5	2	7	6	8	4	3
6	2	3	8	1	4	9	5	7
2	7	9	6	8	1	4	3	5
3	4	8	5	2	9	6	7	1
5	6	1	4	3	7	2	8	9
8	9	2	1	5	3	7	6	4
4	3	7	9	6	8	5	1	2
1	5	6	7	4	2	3	9	8

Puzzle 70

6	2	8	9	4	1	3	7	5
9	3	1	8	5	7	2	4	6
7	4	5	3	2	6	8	9	1
5	1	2	6	7	8	4	3	9
8	6	9	1	3	4	5	2	7
3	7	4	2	9	5	1	6	8
1	8	7	4	6	2	9	5	3
2	9	6	5	1	3	7	8	4
4	5	3	7	8	9	6	1	2

Puzzle 71

9	6	8	4	5	7	1	2	3
1	2	3	6	8	9	4	5	7
7	4	5	1	2	3	6	8	9
5	3	4	8	9	1	7	6	2
6	9	7	5	3	2	8	1	4
8	1	2	7	4	6	3	9	5
2	5	1	3	6	4	9	7	8
3	7	9	2	1	8	5	4	6
4	8	6	9	7	5	2	3	1

Puzzle 72

5	1	2	3	7	8	6	4	9
3	6	7	4	9	1	2	5	8
4	8	9	5	2	6	7	3	1
6	7	4	8	3	5	1	9	2
8	9	3	2	1	4	5	7	6
1	2	5	9	6	7	3	8	4
9	3	8	1	5	2	4	6	7
7	4	1	6	8	3	9	2	5
2	5	6	7	4	9	8	1	3

Puzzle 73

5	6	7	1	8	2	9	3	4
9	2	8	3	4	5	6	1	7
3	1	4	6	9	7	5	8	2
6	4	3	8	7	9	1	2	5
7	5	9	2	1	3	8	4	6
2	8	1	4	5	6	7	9	3
4	7	5	9	2	8	3	6	1
8	3	2	7	6	1	4	5	9
1	9	6	5	3	4	2	7	8

Puzzle 74

2	9	4	3	1	5	6	7	8
3	8	5	4	6	7	9	2	1
6	7	1	8	9	2	3	4	5
5	3	6	9	8	4	7	1	2
7	2	9	1	5	6	8	3	4
4	1	8	7	2	3	5	6	9
8	5	7	2	3	1	4	9	6
9	4	2	6	7	8	1	5	3
1	6	3	5	4	9	2	8	7

Puzzle 75

7	1	5	9	8	2	4	3	6
2	3	4	5	6	7	8	1	9
8	6	9	1	3	4	2	5	7
9	7	8	6	1	3	5	2	4
6	2	1	4	9	5	3	7	8
5	4	3	2	7	8	6	9	1
1	8	6	3	5	9	7	4	2
3	9	2	7	4	6	1	8	5
4	5	7	8	2	1	9	6	3

Puzzle 76

8	7	2	6	9	1	3	5	4
9	4	1	2	3	5	6	8	7
3	5	6	4	7	8	1	9	2
4	8	3	5	1	2	7	6	9
7	1	5	8	6	9	2	4	3
6	2	9	7	4	3	5	1	8
5	3	8	9	2	6	4	7	1
1	6	7	3	8	4	9	2	5
2	9	4	1	5	7	8	3	6

Puzzle 77

2	6	3	4	8	5	7	9	1
7	4	9	1	6	2	5	3	8
5	8	1	9	3	7	4	6	2
4	5	2	3	9	6	8	1	7
8	9	6	2	7	1	3	4	5
1	3	7	5	4	8	6	2	9
3	7	4	8	1	9	2	5	6
9	2	8	6	5	4	1	7	3
6	1	5	7	2	3	9	8	4

Puzzle 78

3	5	4	6	9	7	8	2	1
6	7	1	5	8	2	9	4	3
9	8	2	1	3	4	5	6	7
4	6	5	2	7	3	1	8	9
7	9	3	4	1	8	2	5	6
1	2	8	9	5	6	3	7	4
8	1	6	7	2	9	4	3	5
5	3	7	8	4	1	6	9	2
2	4	9	3	6	5	7	1	8

Puzzle 79

3	1	9	4	2	5	6	7	8
6	4	5	3	7	8	2	9	1
7	8	2	1	9	6	5	3	4
8	3	1	2	4	7	9	5	6
9	2	7	5	6	1	4	8	3
4	5	6	8	3	9	7	1	2
5	6	8	7	1	2	3	4	9
1	9	3	6	5	4	8	2	7
2	7	4	9	8	3	1	6	5

Puzzle 80

1	4	2	8	5	9	3	6	7
3	6	5	1	4	7	8	2	9
8	9	7	3	2	6	5	1	4
6	7	1	2	8	4	9	3	5
5	2	8	9	3	1	7	4	6
9	3	4	7	6	5	1	8	2
2	5	9	4	1	3	6	7	8
4	1	6	5	7	8	2	9	3
7	8	3	6	9	2	4	5	1

Puzzle 81

4	8	3	5	7	6	9	1	2
2	5	9	8	1	4	7	6	3
6	1	7	9	2	3	4	8	5
8	2	1	6	9	5	3	7	4
7	9	4	1	3	8	2	5	6
5	3	6	7	4	2	1	9	8
9	4	5	3	6	7	8	2	1
1	6	2	4	8	9	5	3	7
3	7	8	2	5	1	6	4	9

Puzzle 82

9	3	1	2	6	4	5	7	8
5	4	6	1	7	8	9	2	3
7	8	2	9	5	3	1	4	6
3	5	7	6	1	9	2	8	4
6	9	8	7	4	2	3	5	1
1	2	4	3	8	5	7	6	9
8	6	9	5	2	1	4	3	7
2	7	3	4	9	6	8	1	5
4	1	5	8	3	7	6	9	2

Puzzle 83

8	6	7	2	9	1	5	3	4
9	1	2	3	4	5	6	7	8
3	4	5	7	6	8	9	1	2
4	8	3	5	7	6	1	2	9
1	2	9	8	3	4	7	5	6
5	7	6	9	1	2	8	4	3
7	9	4	6	5	3	2	8	1
2	5	1	4	8	9	3	6	7
6	3	8	1	2	7	4	9	5

Puzzle 84

6	5	7	4	8	9	2	1	3
8	3	9	2	7	1	4	5	6
2	4	1	3	5	6	7	8	9
3	6	2	5	1	7	8	9	4
7	8	4	6	9	2	1	3	5
9	1	5	8	3	4	6	7	2
5	7	6	9	2	8	3	4	1
1	2	3	7	4	5	9	6	8
4	9	8	1	6	3	5	2	7

Puzzle 85

3	8	4	5	6	2	9	1	7
5	9	7	4	8	1	6	2	3
1	2	6	9	3	7	4	8	5
8	1	5	6	7	4	2	3	9
4	3	2	8	5	9	7	6	1
6	7	9	1	2	3	5	4	8
9	4	3	7	1	6	8	5	2
7	5	1	2	4	8	3	9	6
2	6	8	3	9	5	1	7	4

Puzzle 86

8	7	9	4	5	3	1	6	2
3	6	1	7	2	8	9	4	5
2	4	5	6	9	1	8	3	7
9	5	2	1	4	6	3	7	8
1	8	4	3	7	9	2	5	6
6	3	7	2	8	5	4	9	1
5	9	3	8	1	7	6	2	4
7	2	8	9	6	4	5	1	3
4	1	6	5	3	2	7	8	9

Puzzle 87

2	5	3	6	8	4	7	1	9
4	6	7	5	9	1	2	3	8
8	9	1	7	2	3	4	5	6
7	4	8	3	5	6	9	2	1
5	1	6	2	4	9	8	7	3
3	2	9	8	1	7	6	4	5
6	7	5	9	3	2	1	8	4
1	8	2	4	6	5	3	9	7
9	3	4	1	7	8	5	6	2

Puzzle 88

3	7	1	4	5	8	9	6	2
2	8	9	1	6	3	4	7	5
4	5	6	7	9	2	3	8	1
5	4	7	6	8	9	2	1	3
6	9	8	2	3	1	5	4	7
1	2	3	5	7	4	6	9	8
7	1	2	9	4	5	8	3	6
8	6	4	3	2	7	1	5	9
9	3	5	8	1	6	7	2	4

Puzzle 89

9	4	7	5	3	2	6	8	1
8	3	1	6	9	4	5	7	2
5	6	2	7	8	1	9	3	4
1	9	3	2	4	5	7	6	8
2	5	4	8	6	7	1	9	3
6	7	8	9	1	3	2	4	5
3	8	5	1	7	6	4	2	9
4	1	6	3	2	9	8	5	7
7	2	9	4	5	8	3	1	6

Puzzle 90

1	7	8	9	2	3	4	5	6
3	2	6	1	4	5	7	8	9
4	5	9	6	7	8	1	2	3
2	1	4	5	6	7	3	9	8
5	6	7	8	3	9	2	1	4
8	9	3	2	1	4	5	6	7
6	3	5	7	8	1	9	4	2
7	8	1	4	9	2	6	3	5
9	4	2	3	5	6	8	7	1

Puzzle 91

7	5	8	1	9	2	3	4	6
9	1	2	3	4	6	5	7	8
3	6	4	5	7	8	9	1	2
4	7	3	8	1	5	2	6	9
8	9	5	2	6	4	7	3	1
6	2	1	7	3	9	4	8	5
5	8	6	4	2	7	1	9	3
1	4	9	6	5	3	8	2	7
2	3	7	9	8	1	6	5	4

Puzzle 92

7	4	5	2	6	3	9	8	1
6	8	2	1	4	9	5	7	3
1	9	3	8	5	7	2	4	6
3	1	7	4	8	2	6	9	5
8	2	4	5	9	6	1	3	7
5	6	9	3	7	1	4	2	8
9	3	8	6	1	4	7	5	2
4	5	6	7	2	8	3	1	9
2	7	1	9	3	5	8	6	4

Puzzle 93

1	5	4	3	6	7	8	9	2
7	2	8	5	9	1	3	4	6
3	6	9	8	2	4	5	7	1
4	7	2	6	1	3	9	5	8
5	8	1	2	4	9	7	6	3
9	3	6	7	5	8	1	2	4
6	9	5	1	8	2	4	3	7
8	4	3	9	7	6	2	1	5
2	1	7	4	3	5	6	8	9

Puzzle 94

1	8	9	3	2	4	5	6	7
2	7	3	5	1	6	8	9	4
5	4	6	7	8	9	1	2	3
7	6	8	9	3	1	4	5	2
9	1	2	4	5	8	7	3	6
3	5	4	6	7	2	9	8	1
4	3	5	8	6	7	2	1	9
6	9	1	2	4	5	3	7	8
8	2	7	1	9	3	6	4	5

Puzzle 95

8	9	1	7	2	3	4	5	6
5	6	7	4	8	9	1	2	3
2	4	3	1	5	6	7	8	9
9	5	4	2	1	7	6	3	8
6	1	2	5	3	8	9	7	4
7	3	8	6	9	4	2	1	5
1	7	6	8	4	5	3	9	2
3	2	5	9	6	1	8	4	7
4	8	9	3	7	2	5	6	1

Puzzle 96

9	8	6	4	5	7	2	1	3
1	2	3	6	8	9	4	5	7
4	5	7	1	2	3	6	8	9
5	7	8	2	3	1	9	4	6
2	9	1	7	4	6	8	3	5
3	6	4	8	9	5	1	7	2
6	1	9	3	7	4	5	2	8
7	4	2	5	6	8	3	9	1
8	3	5	9	1	2	7	6	4

Puzzle 97

5	8	1	7	9	3	4	2	6
2	4	3	8	1	6	7	9	5
6	7	9	2	4	5	1	3	8
7	6	4	9	5	1	2	8	3
8	9	2	4	3	7	6	5	1
1	3	5	6	2	8	9	7	4
9	1	8	3	6	2	5	4	7
3	2	6	5	7	4	8	1	9
4	5	7	1	8	9	3	6	2

Puzzle 98

2	3	5	7	1	4	6	8	9
4	6	7	5	8	9	1	2	3
8	9	1	2	3	6	4	5	7
3	4	2	6	5	1	7	9	8
5	7	6	8	9	2	3	4	1
9	1	8	3	4	7	5	6	2
7	2	9	4	6	3	8	1	5
1	5	4	9	7	8	2	3	6
6	8	3	1	2	5	9	7	4

Puzzle 99

8	9	1	2	3	4	5	7	6
4	5	3	9	7	6	2	1	8
6	7	2	5	1	8	4	9	3
7	3	5	4	8	2	9	6	1
9	1	4	7	6	3	8	2	5
2	6	8	1	5	9	3	4	7
3	4	6	8	2	7	1	5	9
1	8	9	6	4	5	7	3	2
5	2	7	3	9	1	6	8	4

Puzzle 100

1	7	9	2	3	4	6	5	8
2	8	3	5	9	6	1	4	7
4	5	6	7	1	8	9	2	3
3	6	7	4	5	9	8	1	2
8	9	1	6	7	2	4	3	5
5	2	4	1	8	3	7	9	6
7	3	2	8	4	1	5	6	9
9	4	8	3	6	5	2	7	1
6	1	5	9	2	7	3	8	4

Puzzle 101

2	5	3	4	6	9	7	8	1
9	4	1	2	7	8	6	5	3
7	6	8	3	1	5	9	2	4
1	7	4	5	3	6	8	9	2
3	8	9	7	2	1	4	6	5
5	2	6	8	9	4	1	3	7
4	9	2	6	5	7	3	1	8
6	3	7	1	8	2	5	4	9
8	1	5	9	4	3	2	7	6

Puzzle 102

5	3	2	8	4	6	7	9	1
9	8	1	3	2	7	5	4	6
4	6	7	9	1	5	3	8	2
1	7	6	2	3	4	8	5	9
8	2	9	5	7	1	6	3	4
3	4	5	6	8	9	1	2	7
2	5	4	7	6	8	9	1	3
6	9	3	1	5	2	4	7	8
7	1	8	4	9	3	2	6	5

Puzzle 103

1	8	9	7	2	6	4	3	5
2	3	4	8	1	5	6	7	9
5	6	7	3	9	4	8	1	2
6	9	8	5	3	2	1	4	7
7	4	2	6	8	1	5	9	3
3	5	1	4	7	9	2	6	8
4	2	3	9	6	8	7	5	1
8	7	5	1	4	3	9	2	6
9	1	6	2	5	7	3	8	4

Puzzle 104

8	5	3	4	2	9	1	6	7
6	9	4	1	3	7	2	8	5
1	7	2	5	6	8	9	3	4
7	4	1	9	5	3	6	2	8
5	6	8	2	7	1	3	4	9
2	3	9	8	4	6	7	5	1
3	1	5	6	9	4	8	7	2
4	8	6	7	1	2	5	9	3
9	2	7	3	8	5	4	1	6

Puzzle 105

6	5	7	3	8	9	1	2	4
8	2	9	4	1	5	7	6	3
3	1	4	2	6	7	5	8	9
5	6	2	7	3	8	4	9	1
7	8	1	9	4	2	3	5	6
9	4	3	1	5	6	2	7	8
1	7	5	8	9	4	6	3	2
2	3	8	6	7	1	9	4	5
4	9	6	5	2	3	8	1	7

Puzzle 106

9	3	2	1	6	5	4	8	7
1	4	5	2	7	8	9	6	3
6	8	7	3	9	4	5	1	2
5	7	9	4	8	6	3	2	1
8	1	6	5	2	3	7	4	9
3	2	4	9	1	7	6	5	8
4	9	3	8	5	2	1	7	6
7	5	8	6	3	1	2	9	4
2	6	1	7	4	9	8	3	5

Puzzle 107

3	1	2	6	4	5	7	8	9
9	4	6	8	7	1	2	5	3
5	7	8	3	9	2	1	6	4
8	5	7	4	6	9	3	1	2
1	6	3	7	2	8	9	4	5
2	9	4	1	5	3	8	7	6
4	8	5	2	3	7	6	9	1
6	3	1	9	8	4	5	2	7
7	2	9	5	1	6	4	3	8

Puzzle 108

1	4	6	9	5	2	3	7	8
3	7	9	1	4	8	2	5	6
5	2	8	6	7	3	9	4	1
2	8	3	5	6	4	1	9	7
7	9	4	8	2	1	5	6	3
6	1	5	7	3	9	4	8	2
9	6	7	3	1	5	8	2	4
8	3	2	4	9	6	7	1	5
4	5	1	2	8	7	6	3	9

Puzzle 109

6	2	4	5	8	9	1	7	3
1	5	7	2	3	6	8	4	9
3	8	9	4	1	7	5	2	6
7	9	6	1	2	8	4	3	5
2	1	5	7	4	3	6	9	8
8	4	3	6	9	5	7	1	2
4	6	8	3	7	2	9	5	1
5	7	2	9	6	1	3	8	4
9	3	1	8	5	4	2	6	7

Puzzle 110

7	8	2	9	6	1	3	4	5
5	6	9	7	3	4	8	1	2
3	4	1	5	8	2	9	6	7
8	9	3	4	1	7	2	5	6
4	7	5	6	2	9	1	8	3
2	1	6	8	5	3	7	9	4
6	2	4	1	7	8	5	3	9
9	3	8	2	4	5	6	7	1
1	5	7	3	9	6	4	2	8

Puzzle 111

4	6	8	9	5	7	3	1	2
5	7	9	3	1	2	4	6	8
2	1	3	6	8	4	9	5	7
3	8	6	5	2	9	7	4	1
7	9	2	1	4	3	5	8	6
1	4	5	7	6	8	2	9	3
6	2	7	4	9	1	8	3	5
8	5	4	2	3	6	1	7	9
9	3	1	8	7	5	6	2	4

Puzzle 112

3	7	4	8	9	5	6	1	2
5	9	2	3	6	1	7	8	4
6	8	1	2	4	7	5	9	3
8	3	9	1	5	2	4	6	7
7	1	5	4	8	6	2	3	9
2	4	6	9	7	3	8	5	1
9	6	3	5	2	4	1	7	8
1	2	7	6	3	8	9	4	5
4	5	8	7	1	9	3	2	6

Puzzle 113

9	3	7	1	5	8	2	6	4
8	5	1	6	4	2	7	3	9
2	4	6	7	3	9	8	1	5
3	2	8	4	6	5	9	7	1
6	7	4	8	9	1	3	5	2
5	1	9	2	7	3	4	8	6
7	6	5	9	8	4	1	2	3
1	9	3	5	2	7	6	4	8
4	8	2	3	1	6	5	9	7

Puzzle 114

9	1	7	4	5	3	6	8	2
8	3	6	2	1	7	9	4	5
4	2	5	8	6	9	7	1	3
5	6	4	3	2	8	1	9	7
1	7	8	6	9	5	2	3	4
2	9	3	7	4	1	5	6	8
6	4	9	5	8	2	3	7	1
7	8	2	1	3	6	4	5	9
3	5	1	9	7	4	8	2	6

Puzzle 115

1	3	7	4	5	8	6	2	9
6	5	8	7	9	2	1	3	4
4	9	2	1	3	6	5	7	8
5	7	1	3	2	9	4	8	6
9	2	3	6	8	4	7	5	1
8	4	6	5	7	1	2	9	3
3	6	5	8	1	7	9	4	2
2	8	4	9	6	5	3	1	7
7	1	9	2	4	3	8	6	5

Puzzle 116

3	9	5	6	4	7	8	2	1
4	6	2	8	3	1	5	9	7
1	7	8	9	2	5	3	4	6
2	8	1	5	9	3	6	7	4
9	4	3	7	1	6	2	5	8
6	5	7	2	8	4	9	1	3
7	3	9	1	5	8	4	6	2
5	1	4	3	6	2	7	8	9
8	2	6	4	7	9	1	3	5

Puzzle 117

1	8	4	9	7	3	5	6	2
3	7	9	2	6	5	4	8	1
6	2	5	1	4	8	9	3	7
9	1	7	3	8	4	2	5	6
2	3	8	6	5	1	7	4	9
5	4	6	7	2	9	3	1	8
8	6	2	5	3	7	1	9	4
7	9	3	4	1	6	8	2	5
4	5	1	8	9	2	6	7	3